The Voyages of Sinbad the Sailor

Activity Book

Peter Kipling

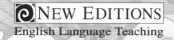

NEW EDITIONS
English Language Teaching

Credits

First published by New Editions 2000

New Editions
37 Bagley Wood Road
Kennington
Oxford OX1 5LY
England

New Editions
PO Box 76101
171 10 Nea Smyrni
Athens
Greece

Tel.: (+30) 210 9883156
Fax: (+30) 210 9880223
E-mail: enquiries@new-editions.com
Website: www.new-editions.com

Text, design and illustrations © New Editions 2000

ISBN   960-7609-92-1

Illustrations by Tim Wilson

Every effort has been made to trace copyright holders.
If any have been inadvertently overlooked, the publishers will be pleased to make the necessary acknowledgements at the first opportunity.

Contents

Activity One
Spot the differences

Can you find the six differences between picture A and picture B?
Work with a friend and see who finishes first in the class.

A

B

1   In picture A Sinbad is wearing a pair of boots.
      In picture B he hasn't got a boot on his right foot.

2   In picture A ....
      In picture B ....

3   In picture A ....
      In picture B ....

4   In picture A ....
      In picture B ....

5   In picture A ....
      In picture B ....

6   In picture A ....
      In picture B ....

Activity Two
Get Me Out of Here!

Help Sinbad get off the deserted island by finding a way through the maze. There are five words inside the maze. Write down each word as you come to it. If you go through the maze correctly, the words will make a sentence.

What is the sentence?

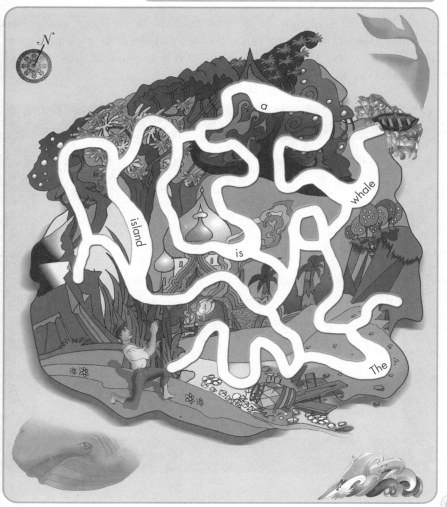

Activity Three
Magical Creatures

Many adventures have magical creatures in them. Some are like normal animals but much bigger (for example, Rocs are like eagles, but larger). Others are different parts of things together (for example, centaurs are half-human and half-horse).

Invent a magical creature of your own. Give the creature a name. Draw a picture of it, and then write a short description of the animal. What does it look like? Is it friendly or dangerous? Is it clever or not? What does it like to eat? Where does your creature live?

My magical creature is called

Activity Four
Island Shopping

If you owned a shop, what would you like to sell?

1 First, decide what kind of shop you want.

2 Next, make a list of what you want to sell in your shop.

3 Be sure to write down how much each thing will cost.

4 Make a poster showing the things you want to sell, along with the prices.

5 Finally, invite other students to your store.
   Have a dialogue asking them:
   • Do you want to buy anything?
   • Who do you want to buy it for?
   • How much do you want to spend?
   and so on.

List   Cost

....

....

....

....

....

....

Poster

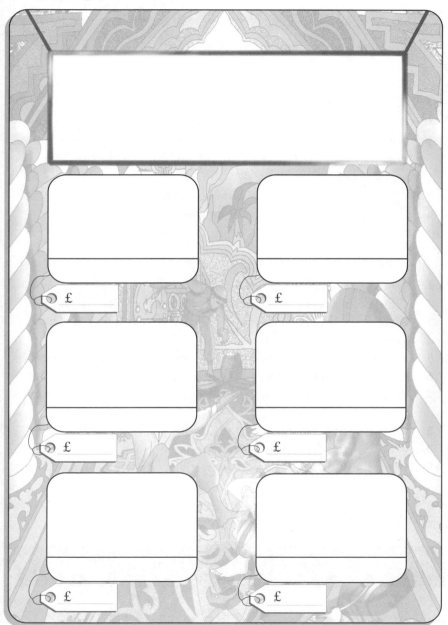

Activity Five
Don't Eat the Food!

You will need dice, counters or buttons

Rules of the Game
1   Throw a six to start. Then throw again.
2   When you land on a number square, answer the question from below. If you answer the question correctly, take another turn.
3   When you land on a food square, miss a turn.
4   The first person to finish is the winner.

Questions
1   What is Sinbad the Porter's job?
2   Why does the big whale that looks like an island wake up?
3   What does Sinbad make for the king who is proud of his horses?
4   What is the white dome?
5   In the valley of the diamonds, where does Sinbad sleep?
6   How does Sinbad get out of the valley of the diamonds?
7   What kind of building does Sinbad find on the ape-men's island?
8   Why doesn't the giant eat Sinbad?
9   Why doesn't Sinbad eat the food?
10 Who shows Sinbad how to leave the city of the naked men?

Activity Six

Sinbad's problem

Connect the dots and then write the two sentences you find.

Activity Seven
The Code

Sinbad has landed on an island. Someone has put a sign on the beach to help him, but it is in a secret code. Help Sinbad find out what the sign says! Look at the letters below. They don't seem to make any sense, but follow the instructions, and the words will become a sentence!

DZCSBRMAXWUZYMXWVMUTSRMQP

1   First, cross out all the 'M's.
2   Second, change the 'P' to a 'T'.
3   Now change the 'Q' to an 'H'.
4   Change both 'R's to 'E's.
5   Make both 'S's into 'O's.
6   Make the 'T' into 'L'.
7   Make the 'U's into 'D's.
8   Replace the 'V' with 'M'.
9   Replace the 'W's with 'A's.
10 Turn the 'X's into 'N's.
11 Turn the 'Y' into an 'I'.
12 Turn the 'Z's into 'S's.
13 Change the 'A' to a 'G'.
14 Replace the 'B' with 'R'.
15 Turn the 'C' into a 'U'.
16 Now write all your new letters down again from back to front.
17 Change the 'D' to a full stop.
18 Read your sentence!

Try to make up a code of your own if you can. Write a short message to a friend in your new code, and then explain to him/her how to read it!

Activity Eight

Invent your own adventure for Sinbad.
Here are some ideas to help you:

Paragraph 3

Describe the island.
What did it look like?
Did it have food and water?
Were there people there?
Were there monsters?

Paragraph 4

Describe Sinbad's problem.
Describe how Sinbad got out of the problem.
How did he find a ship to go home?

When you have written your story, read it to your friend and then ask if he/she liked it. Then listen to your friend's story.

Sinbad was home again, but he didn't feel relaxed.
He wanted to go to sea again, so he found a ship and left.

At first the trip was very nice, but then a storm came and destroyed his ship. Sinbad was in trouble again. He took hold of a piece of wood and floated on it for three days until he came to an island.

The island was

Sinbad didn't know what to do.

He

Finally, Sinbad reached his nice comfortable house. Home at last! 'I'll never go on another adventure,' Sinbad said. But he was wrong again!

Bestseller Readers

Level 2

The Voyages of Sinbad the Sailor

Suddenly, I heard the captain shout, 'Look out! Run for your lives! This island isn't really an island. It's a huge whale in the middle of the sea. It was asleep when we came, but the fires woke it up.'

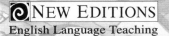
NEW EDITIONS
English Language Teaching

ISBN 960-7609-92-1
9 789607 609922